This Book Belongs To:

....

Made in United States
North Haven, CT
22 June 2023

38009073R00070